Scales & Arpeggios

Piano

Grade 5

Good legato, even fingers, firm tone and a musical curve are the essential features for playing scales and arpeggios well.

The suggested fingering shown here is not obligatory; any practical and systematic fingering which produces a good result will be accepted in the examination. Some alternative fingering is shown as follows: 4/3. In the playing of arpeggios, the decision as to which fingering to adopt will depend on the size and shape of the player's hand. Examiners do not comment on the choice of fingering unless it interferes with an even, legato flow.

To save space, the three-octave scales are printed over two octaves only; these may, however, be grouped in threes in performance.

In the examination, all scales and arpeggios must be played from memory.

Metronome marks shown here indicate *minimum* recommended speeds for the examination.

Reference must always be made to the syllabus for the year in which the examination is to be taken, in case any changes have been made to the requirements.

The Associated Board of the Royal Schools of Music

Major and Minor Scales (melodic *or* harmonic at candidate's choice) in similar motion

Hands separately and together an octave apart: 3 octaves: ♩ = 63

3 octaves

3

3 octaves

E major

E minor melodic

or

E minor harmonic

B major

B minor melodic

or

B minor harmonic

4

3 octaves

F♯ major (enharmonic G♭)

F♯ minor melodic

or

F♯ minor harmonic

D♭ major (enharmonic C♯)

C♯ minor melodic

or

C♯ minor harmonic

3 octaves

Ab major

G♯ minor melodic (enharmonic Ab)

or

G♯ minor harmonic (enharmonic Ab)

Eb major

Eb minor melodic

or

Eb minor harmonic

3 octaves

7

Major and Harmonic Minor Scales (Group 1 *or* 2 at candidate's choice) in contrary motion
Hands together beginning and ending on the key-note (unison): 2 octaves: ♩ = 63

GROUP 1

A major

F major

D♭ major (enharmonic C♯)

A minor

F minor

C♯ minor

or GROUP 2

D major

F♯ major (enharmonic G♭)

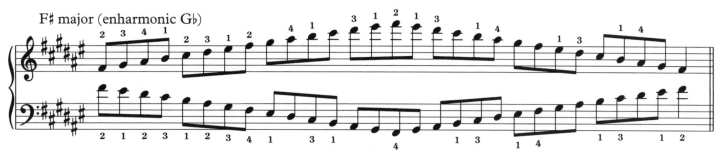

B♭ major

D minor

F♯ minor

B♭ minor

9

Chromatic Scales in similar motion

Hands separately and together an octave apart: beginning on any note named by the examiner

3 octaves: ♩ = 72

This example is a guide

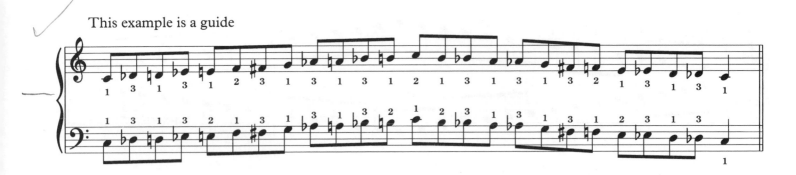

Chromatic Scales in contrary motion

Hands together beginning and ending on the same note (unison): 2 octaves: ♩ = 72

Beginning on D

Beginning on A♭

Arpeggios of major and minor common chords in root position
Hands separately and together an octave apart: 2 octaves: ♩ = 88

F♯ major (enharmonic G♭)

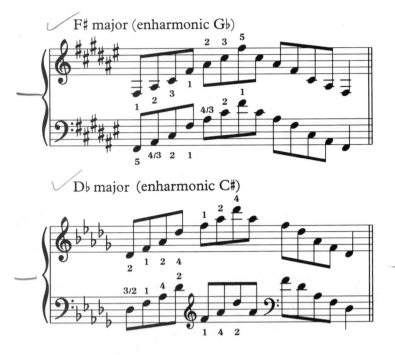

F♯ minor

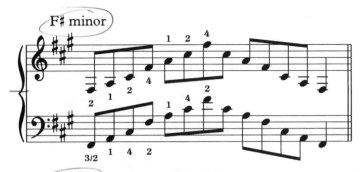

D♭ major (enharmonic C♯)

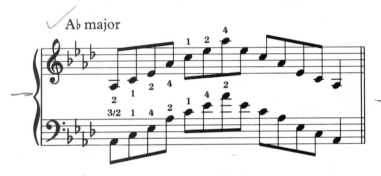

C♯ minor

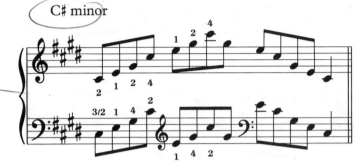

A♭ major

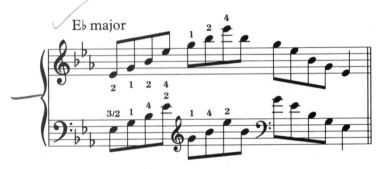

G♯ minor (enharmonic A♭)

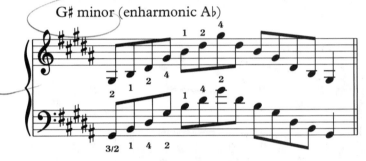

E♭ major

E♭ minor

B♭ major

B♭ minor

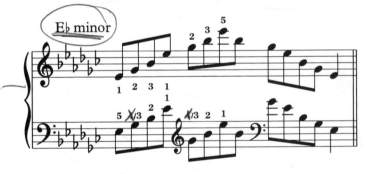

F major

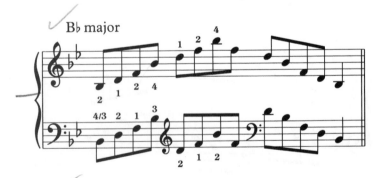

F minor

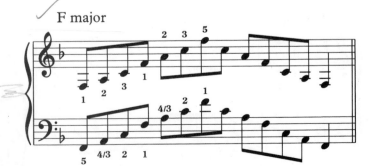

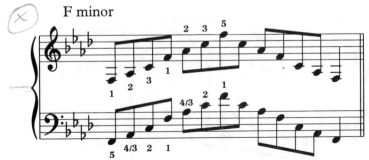

Printed in Great Britain by Headley Brothers Ltd., The Invicta Press, Ashford, Kent.

2:06